Music
and My
Favorite Things

Companion Songbook

Linda Swears

Lorna Lutz Heyge

Kindermusik® International
Greensboro, North Carolina, U.S.A.

Published: 1994, 1991 by Kindermusik® International, Inc.

ISBN 0-945613-20-2

Printed in U.S.A.

Every reasonable effort has been taken to trace ownership of copyrighted material and to make due acknowledgment. We believe the remaining material to be in the public domain. Any errors or omissions will be gladly rectified in future editions.

Credits:
With My Baby on My Knee and *Peek-a-Boo* are New England nursery songs from the private collection of Luella DuWors.

MUSIC AND MY FAVORITE THINGS

Songs, chants, dances, and musical play about toys, stuffed animals,
and other special things and people in a child's world.

The most important learning environment for your child is your home. A family lifestyle that includes music and movement in a joyful, playful atmosphere draws forth the innate musical gifts of even the youngest child. The *Kindermusik Family Packet* has been designed to encourage musical interaction and exploration at home.

This *Companion Songbook*, provided for your use throughout the week, will refresh your memory of class experiences. It will also give you specific ideas about how to recreate the joyful exchange you and your child shared in the Kindermusik group session.

The child's *Picture Songbook* reminds children of pleasurable class activities. Its bright, sensitive watercolor drawings express the themes of many shared songs, chants, and dances. Enjoy the details of the pictures and sing your favorite songs as you sit and look at the book together with your child.

The professionally produced *Home Cassette* provides a wide variety of quality vocal examples for your child. Solo selections sung by children, as well as the works of a children's choir, adult vocalists, and accomplished instrumentalists have been carefully chosen for your repeated listening pleasure. Singing, playing, and dancing to the music on the cassette will become a continuing pleasure for you and your child.

Set aside a regular opportunity for making music together, and enjoy those special times when music "just happens." Sing with your child. The cassette tape is an excellent model, but your live performance is the most important example for your child. Make up songs and encourage your child's vocal experimentation. Move with your child, and strengthen that loving, trusting connection so vital at this early stage of life.

If possible, have instruments available for exploration and use at home. Let your child see that music is a normal and spontaneous part of existence. Above all, enjoy making music together.

Clap Hello

The tune of this song is from "Old Joe Clarke," a well-known square-dance tune from Tennessee. The lively rhythmic character of the song invites all kinds of motions. Try "Wave, wave, wave hello. Wave hello to Mommy...," "Tap, tap, tap hello. Tap hello to Grandpa...," and so forth.

Clap, clap, clap hel – lo. Clap hel – lo to – geth – er.

Fine

Clap, clap, clap hel – lo. Clap hel – lo to – geth – er.

La, la, la, la, la, la, la, la, la, la, la, la, la,

D.C. al Fine

la, la, la, la, la, la, la, la, la, la, la, la.

The Bear Went Over the Mountain

This is a wonderful song for bouncing. Bouncing songs are especially important both because they are stimulating and because they allow you to give your child a feeling of beat in the whole body. In the middle section of the song, add a motion to pretend that you are looking around with binoculars.

The bear went o-ver the moun-tain, The bear went o-ver the moun-tain. The bear went o-ver the moun-tain, To see what he could see. To

see what he could see. To see what he could see. The

bear went o - ver the moun - tain, The bear went o - ver the moun - tain. The

bear went o - ver the moun - tain, To see what he could see.

vs. 2: The other side of the mountain,
Was all that he could see.

Teddy Bear

Think up other actions for the teddy bear to do. Your child will enjoy making suggestions and acting them out. Add your own ideas in the blanks during the third verse on the recording.

Ted-dy Bear, Ted-dy Bear, turn a - round, Ted-dy Bear, Ted-dy Bear,

touch the ground, Ted-dy Bear, Ted-dy Bear, show your shoe,

Ted - dy Bear, Ted - dy Bear, that will do.

vs. 2: Teddy Bear, Teddy Bear, brush your hair,
Teddy Bear, Teddy Bear, climb the stair,
Teddy Bear, Teddy Bear, reach for the sky,
Teddy Bear, Teddy Bear, wave goodbye.

Bill Anderson

Enjoy this little verse during changing and dressing time. Grasp your child's legs at the ankles, calling one leg Bill Anderson and the other Tom Sim. Lift one leg over the other faster and faster until the last line. At the words "They fell down the hill!", gently roll the child's legs over his/her head.

This is Bill Anderson,
This is Tom Sim.
Tom called Bill to play
And fell over him.
Bill over Tom,
And Tom over Bill,
Over and over
They fell down the hill!

Let Ev'ryone Clap

Songs that give directions are particularly appealing to young children. Learning words and acting them out is a special joy during this period of fascination with language. This song also encourages you to experiment with your voice—whispering, laughing, and calling out. What other sounds can you add?

Let ev – 'ry – one clap hands with me. (clap, clap) Let

ev – 'ry – one clap hands with me. (clap, clap) Come

on and join in the game. (clap, clap) You'll

find that it's al – ways the same. (clap, clap)

vs. 2:   Let ev'ryone whisper with me. (Sh, Sh)
vs. 3:   Let ev'ryone laugh with me. (Ha! Ha!)
vs. 4:   Let ev'ryone call out with me. (Whoopee!)

Cindy

Folksongs from the southern mountains are a rich part of the American heritage.
Listen to the banjo in the recording.

I wish I was an ap – ple, A – hang-in' on a tree, And
ev – 'ry time my Cin – dy passed, She'd take a bite of me.

Refrain

Git a-long home, Cin – dy, Cin – dy, Git a-long home, Cin – dy, Cin – dy,
Git a-long home, Cin – dy, Cin – dy, I'll mar – ry you some day.

Hush, Little Baby

Singing lullabies can add a special, tender touch to bedtime. This lovely song from
Alabama is becoming a favorite in many families. Our recording uses an instrumental arrangement with flute, harp, and cello.

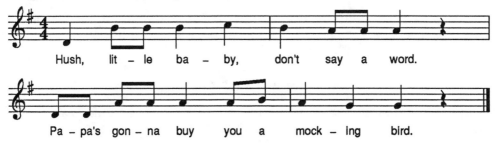

Hush, lit – le ba – by, don't say a word.
Pa – pa's gon – na buy you a mock – ing bird.

vs. 2: If that mocking bird won't sing,
Papa's gonna buy you a diamond ring.

vs. 3: If that diamond ring turns brass,
Papa's gonna buy you a lookin' glass.

vs. 4: If that lookin' glass gets broke,
Papa's gonna buy you a billy goat.

vs. 5: If that billy goat won't pull,
Papa's gonna buy you a cart and bull.

vs. 6: If that cart and bull turn over,
Papa's gonna buy you a dog named Rover.

vs. 7: If that dog named Rover won't bark,
Papa's gonna buy you a horse and cart.

vs. 8: If that horse and cart fall down,
You'll still be the sweetest little baby in town.

Quickly, Slowly

Words expressing opposites are great fun for young children. Chant this verse expressively and enjoy crawling around on the floor with your child.

Quickly, quickly, very quickly,
Runs the little mouse.
Quickly, quickly, very quickly,
All around the house.

Slowly, slowly, very slowly,
Crawls the garden snail.
Slowly, slowly, very slowly,
Along the wooden rail.

Music for Rhythm Sticks

How many ways can you tap the rhythm sticks? Tap them high in the air, on the floor, on your knees, and so on. Take turns with your child finding new ways to play the rhythm sticks along with this recording.

Jimmy Crack Corn

This American circle game has a delightful tune and simple actions. Make such singing games a part of your family gatherings. Not only is it fun for young and old to sing and move together, but shared activities bond relationships and produce happy memories.

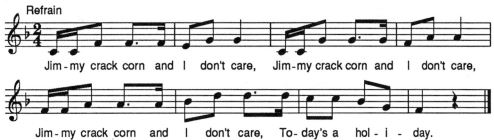

Jim-my crack corn and I don't care, Jim-my crack corn and I don't care,

Jim-my crack corn and I don't care, To-day's a hol-i-day.

vs. 1:   Both hands up and I don't care... *Refrain*
vs. 2:   Round and round and I don't care... *Refrain*
          Turn on the spot.
vs. 3:   Jump up and down and I don't care... *Refrain*

In the Hoop

A hoop is a wonderful device to help children understand space and relationships. Give your child a big hug when you are both in the hoop.

You are in the hoop now.   *Place hoop over child.*
I am in the hoop now.   *Place hoop over self.*
We are in the hoop now.   *Place hoop over self and child together.*

Pop Goes the Weasel

Use the hoop to play the game you learned in class. Walk around the hoop while you are singing, and then "pop" into it at the appropriate place.

The tune for this song dates back to England in 1853. It was used for a dance at "Her Majesty's & The Nobilities Balls," which became popular throughout England.

All a-round the cob-bler's bench, The mon-key chased the wea-sel, The

mon-key thought 'twas lots of fun, Pop! goes the wea-sel.

When the Train Comes Along

Making the sounds and motion of a moving train is lots of fun for everyone. Include this song from South Carolina in your family parties. Consider making rattles to play along. Plastic Easter eggs are an ideal size for your child's hands and can be filled with uncooked rice, split peas, lentils, or something similar.

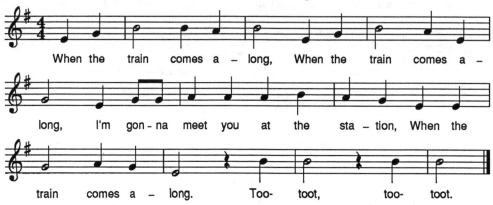

When the train comes a - long, When the train comes a - long, I'm gon - na meet you at the sta - tion, When the train comes a - long. Too- toot, too- toot.

vs. 2: Gonna catch me a ride,
Gonna catch me a ride,
Gonna catch me a ride to the mountains,
When the train comes along.
Too- toot, too- toot.

vs. 3: I'll be back soon again,
I'll be back soon again,
I'll be back to see you Mama,
When the train comes along.
Too- toot, too- toot.

Dance Little Dolly

This is another marvelous song for bouncing. When your child is a little older, encourage him/her to bounce a favorite doll or stuffed animal. Add verses such as "Dance little teddy" or "Dance little (child's name)."

Dance lit - tle dol - ly, dance lit - tle dol - ly. This way, that way, this way, that way. Up - si, up - si, up - si, dai - sy oh!

Five Kittens/I Love Little Kitty

Finger plays bring the children's attention to small muscle movements and help them to gain control. In this verse, your child can practice independent finger motion while making a delightful "meow" sound.

Five little kittens,   *Hold up five fingers.*
All black and white,
Sleeping very soundly,   *Make a fist.*
All through the night.
Meow, meow, meow, meow, meow,   *Raise a finger for each*
It's time to get up now.   *"meow."*

I love lit – tle kit – ty, her coat is so warm, And
if I don't hurt her, she'll do me no harm.

With My Baby on My Knee

When you sing and rock your child, you touch him/her in significant ways: with your arms and body, and with your voice. Substitute your child's name for the word "baby" in this song.

With my ba – by on my knee, Tra la la,
la la la, I'm as hap – py as can be, Tra la la,
la la la, With my ba – by on my knee, Tra la la,
la la la, La la la la la la la la la.

Peek-a-Boo

Use transparent scarves to play a peek-a-boo game while you sing this song.

Peek - a - boo! I see you, I see you
hid - ing there, La la la la la, peek - a - boo!
I see you, I see you hid - ing there! _____

I Have a Little Dolly

Songs that give your child an opportunity to fill in words or actions encourage early participation. Find your own toy microphone at home and let your child respond with the "dolly" sounds.

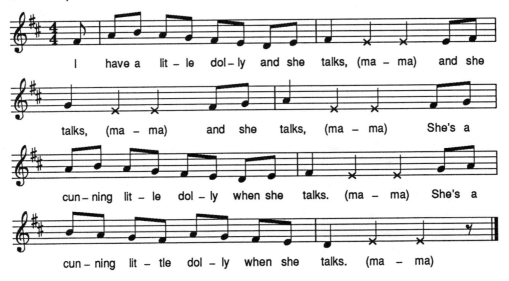

I have a lit - le dol - ly and she talks, (ma - ma) and she
talks, (ma - ma) and she talks, (ma - ma) She's a
cun - ning lit - le dol - ly when she talks. (ma - ma) She's a
cun - ning lit - tle dol - ly when she talks. (ma - ma)

vs. 2:   I have a little dolly and she cries (boo- hoo) ...
vs. 3:   I have a little dolly and she claps (clap, clap) ...

Higgelty, Piggelty

Bouncing is a good activity for this traditional nursery rhyme from the early 1800s. "Pop" your child gently through your legs on the last word; he/she will look forward to that "surprise" each time.

> Higgelty, piggelty, pop!
> The dog has eaten the mop.
> The pig's in a hurry,
> The cat's in a flurry,
> Higgelty, piggelty, pop!

All Around the Kitchen

This splendid folksong from Alabama gives you a fine opportunity to move around the house. Let your child have a chance to be the leader!

On the *Home Cassette*, you can hear an arrangement using violin, harmonica, and piano.

All a-round the kit-chen, cock-a doo-dle doo-dle doo,

All a-round the kit-chen, cock-a doo-dle doo-dle doo.

Now you do like this, cock-a doo-dle doo-dle doo.

Then you do like this, cock-a doo-dle doo-dle doo.

Circus Movements

Just about everyone loves the sights and sounds of the circus! This is a story without words, in which the music on the *Home Cassette* tells the story. Act it out with your child as you tell the story in your own words. Listen for the following sections:

Drum signal	*Let's go to the circus.*
Carousel music	*Take a ride on the carousel.*
Drum signal	*Here come the elephants.*
Slow, heavy music	*They're walking around.*
Drum signal	*Look at the monkeys.*
Bouncy music	*They jump up and down and*
Descending music	*fall to the ground.*

The Merry-Go-Round

Join hands and sing this song to the tune of "The Mulberry Bush."

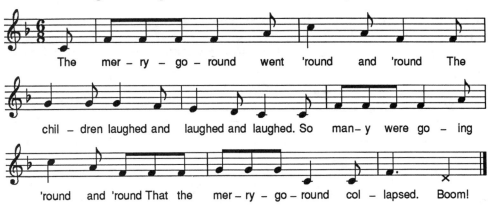

The mer–ry–go–round went 'round and 'round The chil–dren laughed and laughed and laughed. So man–y were go–ing 'round and 'round That the mer–ry–go–round col–lapsed. Boom!

"Hammer" on the floor to rebuild the merry-go-round as you say this chant.

Rat-a-tat-tat.	Rat-a-tat-tat.
Rat-a-tat-tat.	Rat-a-tat-tat.
We'll build you up	Up, up, up, and
With a rat-a-tat-tat.	Away we go!

Country fairs still have carousels. Take your child for a ride on one. Be sure to look at the colorful picture of a traditional carousel in the *Picture Songbook*.

Little Cuckoo

Toy microphones encourage children to make a solo response by showing whose turn it is. Use a mallet or a rhythm stick for a microphone when you sing this song, or buy an inexpensive microphone and cut off the cord.

Stretch Up Very Tall

Sing this song slowly as you act it out with your child. It will help him/her understand "up" and "down" in relation to his/her own body.

Hickory Dickory Dock

Mother Goose rhymes like this verse are a wonderful part of our heritage. In class, the teacher will place the drum in front of a child just in time for him/her to play in the rests. Try this game at home.

Hick-o-ry Dick-o-ry Dock. The mouse ran up the clock. The clock struck one, the mouse ran down. Hick-o-ry Dick-o-ry Dock.

Clock Chant

Rocking back and forth is a motion that young children enjoy, and it stimulates the whole body. Rock in various ways as you chant. Try holding your child in your lap and rocking from side to side, standing and rocking from one foot to the other, or holding hands with your child and rocking from side to side.

> Tick-tock, tick-tock,
> Goes my daddy's big clock.
> Tick-tock, tick-tock,
> Goes my daddy's big clock.
>
> But my mommy's little clock goes
> Tick-tock, tick-tock, tick-tock, tick-tock.

The Blackbird

Sing and tap along with jingle bells, rhythm sticks, or a drum to the recording of this song. You may want to try dancing to the lively sounds of the accordion, violin, and piano. This tune is from an Appalachian folksong.

The Old Woman's Pig

Your child will enjoy making the animal sounds in this American folksong from Texas. Add more verses about your family's favorite animals.

vs. 2: There was an old woman and she had a little cat, meow, meow, meow.
There was an old woman and she had a little cat,
He didn't cost much 'cause he wasn't very fat, meow, meow, meow.

vs. 3: There was an old woman and she had a little frog, croak, croak, croak.
There was an old woman and she had a little frog,
He didn't cost much 'cause she found him in a bog, croak, croak, croak.

Down in Alabama

Activities using hoops help children experience how their bodies are situated in relation to external objects. The text of this delightful tune from Ohio encourages children to explore relationships such as in/out, over/under, and through.

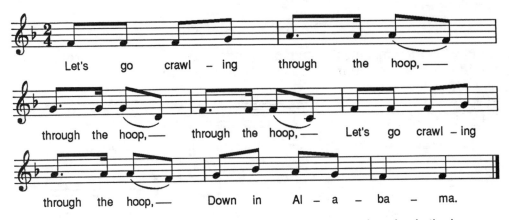

Let's go crawl – ing through the hoop, —— through the hoop, —— through the hoop, —— Let's go crawl – ing through the hoop, —— Down in Al – a – ba – ma.

vs. 2: Let's go walking 'round the hoop...   vs. 3: Let's go jumping in the hoop...

There's a Little Wheel

Appalachia is the source for this American folksong. In class, we accompanied it on resonator bells. Try these at home. If you do not have resonator bells, put dots on the *d* and *a* of a piano or other keyboard instrument and play these notes to accompany your singing.

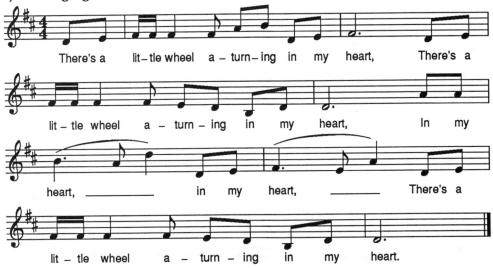

There's a lit – tle wheel a – turn – ing in my heart, There's a lit – tle wheel a – turn – ing in my heart, In my heart, in my heart, There's a lit – tle wheel a – turn – ing in my heart.

vs. 2: There's a little bell a ringing in my heart...
vs. 3: There's a little song a singing in my heart...

Dance with Me

Join hands with family and friends for another dance. Circle as you sing the first part. Stop to carry out the actions of foot tapping and hand clapping, and then join hands to take three steps into the circle and three steps out. Turn around merrily!

Come a-long and dance with me. La, la, la, la, la, la, la,

la, la, la, la, la, la. Come a-long and dance with me.

With your foot you tap, tap, tap. With your hands you clap, clap, clap.

1, 2, 3, 1, 2, 3, 'Round and 'round so mer – ri – ly.

Bim Bam

Sing this beautiful song with many different rocking motions. Children especially love to join both hands with an adult and rock from side to side. Try waving scarves while you sing.

Bim bam bi- ri, bi - ri, bam, bi - ri, bi - ri, bim- bam, bi- ri, bi - ri, bam.

Bim bam _____, Bim bam _____, bim- bam, bi- ri, bi - ri, bam.

Bim bam _____, Bim bam _____, bim- bam bi - ri, bi - ri bam.

Golden Slumbers

This is a traditional English lullaby that is particularly beautiful. Sing along with the *Home Cassette* until it becomes part of your own lullaby repertoire. The recording uses an arrangement with flute, harp, and glockenspiel.

Gol – den slum – bers kiss your eyes, Smiles a – wait you when you rise; Sleep, now my lit – tle one do not cry, And I will sing a lul – la – by.

Santa Maloney

Join hands and swing your arms to this tune. Make up your own verses about other actions.

Refrain

Here we go San-ta Ma – lon – ey, Here we go San-ta Ma – lon – ey, Here we go San-ta Ma – lon – ey, As we go 'round a – bout.

vs. 1: Put your hands out before you. *Refrain*
vs. 2: Put your hands behind you. *Refrain*
vs. 3: Put your hands on your shoulders. *Refrain*

Jumping Jack

Every aspect of this song is inviting to your child. The melody is easy for a child to master, and the word "boing" is especially fun to sing and say. Jumping is a favorite action and stopping is great fun!

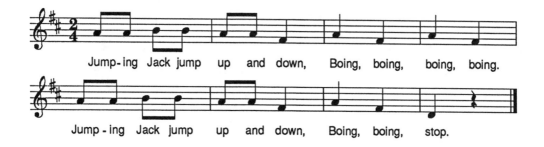

Jump-ing Jack jump up and down, Boing, boing, boing, boing.

Jump-ing Jack jump up and down, Boing, boing, stop.

Mama Paquita

This delightful carnival song from Brazil lends itself beautifully to playing rattle instruments and dancing.

Ma - ma Pa - qui - ta, Ma - ma Pa - qui - ta, Ma - ma Pa -
qui - ta, Ma - ma Pa - qui - ta, Ma - ma Pa -

qui - ta, buy your ba- by a pa- pa - ya, A ripe pa - pa - ya,
qui - ta says, "I have-n't an - y mon- ey to buy pa - pa- yas

and a ba - na - na, A ripe ba - na - na that your
and ripe ba - na - nas. Let's go to car - ni - val and

ba - by will en - joy, Ma - ma, Ma - ma, Ma - ma Pa -
dance the night a -   way!"

Index of Songs, Chants, and Movement Stories

The "Music and My Favorite Things" Home Cassette

Most of the songs, chants, and activities in this *Companion Songbook* are recorded on the *Home Cassette*. However, they do not appear in the same order as in the book; the cassette and book are intended to be used separately. The cassette also includes some rhythm and tonal patterns, each with a pause for echoing, as well as music for dancing. The cassette includes the following:

Clap Hello
Teddy Bear
The Bear Went Over the Mountain
Let Ev'ryone Clap
Rhythm Patterns
Jimmy Crack Corn
Bill Anderson
J. Strauss, Jr., "Blue Danube Waltz"
  (excerpt)
When the Train Comes Along
Hush, Little Baby
Pop Goes the Weasel
Music For Rhythm Sticks
I Have a Little Dolly
Dance Little Dolly
Tonal Patterns
Cindy
Five Kittens/I Love Little Kitty
Roger, "New Orleans Bounce"
  (excerpt)
Higgelty, Piggelty
All Around the Kitchen

Santa Maloney
With My Baby On My Knee/Peek-a-Boo
Circus Movements
The Merry-Go-Round
Little Cuckoo
Rhythm Patterns
Clock Chant
Hickory Dickory Dock
The Blackbird
Stretch Up Very Tall
There's a Little Wheel
Bim Bam
Tonal Patterns
Down in Alabama
Bach, "Minuet in G, No. 4"
  (from *Anna Magdalena's Notebook*)
Jumping Jack
Dance with Me
The Old Woman's Pig
Golden Slumbers
Mama Paquita
Mexican Hat Dance (excerpt)

The Authors and Project Team

Linda Swears is author of *Growing with Kindermusik*, as well as a music educator, composer, and clinician. After more than twenty years work in the field, she is widely recognized as a specialist in the child's voice. She is the author of *Teaching the Elementary School Chorus* and *Discovering the Guitar*. Mrs. Swears was also a consulting author for the Silver Burdett and Ginn music education curriculum series *WORLD OF MUSIC*. Mrs. Swears earned her Bachelor of Music degree from Michigan State University and her Master's degree from Central Michigan

University. She is currently Coordinator of Music in Early Childhood at the Wilmington Music School in Wilmington, Delaware, where she teaches children eighteen months through ten years of age and directs the work of the Early Childhood Teaching Faculty.

Lorna Lutz Heyge is coauthor of the *Kindermusik for the Young Child* program. Her work with young children began in 1971 when she assisted in the development of a music curriculum in cooperation with the West German Association of Youth Music Schools. Dr. Heyge holds a Bachelor of Music degree from the Eastman School of Music, a Master of Music degree from Northwestern University, and a PhD in Musicology from the University of Cologne. She is Music Consultant for the Toronto Montessori Schools.

Audrey Sillick, contributor, is coauthor of the *Kindermusik for the Young Child* program, and the founder of the Toronto Montessori Training Institute. She is an acknowledged authority on the growth and educational development of the child from birth to six years, with a special interest in movement and the acquisition of language.

Deborah and Allan Drew-Brooke-Cormack are Toronto-area artists and illustrators who have created all of the artwork for both this curriculum and *Kindermusik for the Young Child*. Their exceptional ability to give visual expression to the authors' text while maintaining an independent artistic viewpoint is a highlight of this curriculum. Allan does the expressive line drawings and Deborah adds the exquisite watercolor paintings.

Howard Baer has produced all of the recordings that accompany this curriculum. He has also composed much of the music, arranged the instrumental accompaniments, and contributed as a performer. In the field of music education, Mr. Baer has produced recordings for Silver Burdett and Ginn, GLC Publishers, and Berandol Music, and was the arranger, composer, and producer of the audio cassettes that are a part of *Kindermusik for the Young Child*. Among the twenty TV and film scores Mr. Baer has composed, two of the most notable are the 1988 Olympic Games theme for the CBC and musical arrangements for the film *Peter Ustinov in China*. Mr. Baer's credits include four nominations for the coveted Canadian Juno award.

Lynda Powell: Design, Production, and Typesetting

Kathleen Roulston: Editor

Kent Mason: Music Notation